"No act of kindness,
no matter how small,
is ever wasted."

Aesop

"The only time we suffer is when
we believe a thought that argues with
what is. When the mind is perfectly
clear, 'what is' is what we want."

Byron Katie

"Mindfulness means paying attention in particular way; on purpose, in the present moment, and non-judgmentally."

Jon Kabat-Zinn

"We know what we are,
but know not what we may be."

William Shakespeare

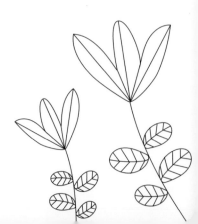

"If you want to conquer the
anxiety of life, live in the moment,
live in the breath."

Amit Ray

"When you realise nothing is lacking,
the whole world belongs to you."

Lao Tzu

"Practice presence – embrace
the place where life happens."

Eckhart Tolle

"Don't let yesterday
use up too much of today."

Cherokee Indian Proverb

"Water, if you don't stir it, will
become clear; the mind left unaltered
will find its own natural peace."

Unknown

"Nature does not hurry,
yet everything is accomplished."

Lao Tzu

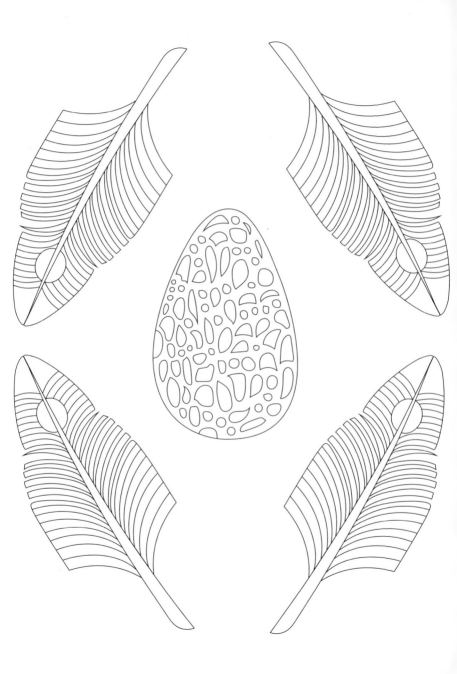

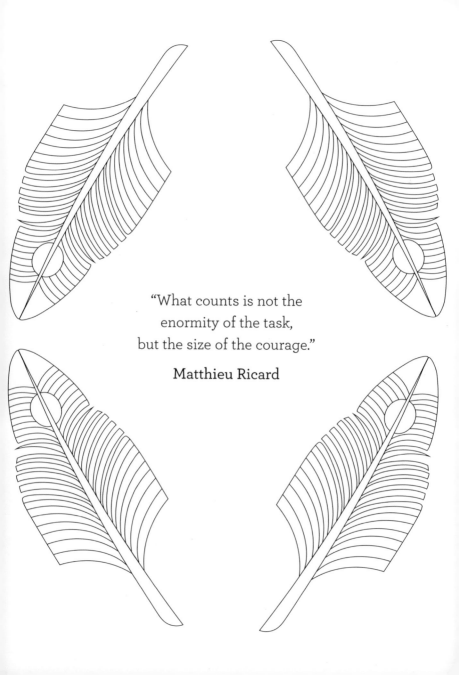

"What counts is not the
enormity of the task,
but the size of the courage."

Matthieu Ricard

"We must not allow the clock
and the calendar to blind us to
the fact that each moment of life
is a miracle and mystery."

H. G. Wells

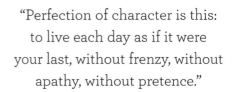

"Perfection of character is this:
to live each day as if it were
your last, without frenzy, without
apathy, without pretence."

Marcus Aurelius